PAINT PROBLEMS

How many things can you find wrong in this picture?

Illustrated by Anni Matsick

FOUR-LETTER WORDS

Most of the words that will answer these clues contain just four letters.
Don't forget to forge ahead and put your answers in the boxes forthwith.

ACROSS

1. Place to swim, bigger than a pond
3. Line in your hair or a role in a play
5. Jump off a board into water
6. Symbol of a country
9. Where you live, your local _____
12. Playing piece for Scrabble or Mahjong
13. Street or highway
14. Abbreviation for mountain
15. Abbreviation for light or lieutenant
16. Dog's name or a small dot
18. As well, too
20. Goat with backward-rolling horns
21. Wander about
24. Stand in this while waiting to gain entrance
27. Without cost
28. Not odd

DOWN

1. Pick up
2. The very end
3. One fruit that sounds like two
4. Frog relative
7. Not rigid
8. Voice range below soprano
10. Turn end over end for this bagel relative
11. Diner sign for food
16. Ride the waves on a board
17. Minutes, hours, days
18. What holds the wheels on a car
19. Not shut
22. Abbreviation for Oregon
23. First two vowels
25. Four in Roman numerals
26. Abbreviation for Northeast

Illustrated by Jon Nez

Answer on page 47.

ROUTE TO THE RING

Find the path that will get Rock Rogan to the ring in time for his big match with Steamroller Smith.

Illustrated by Charles Jordan

Answer on page 47.

QUEST WHO?

Once upon a time, four knights went out on different quests. One went to rescue a princess, one wanted to find the missing Grail, one captured a dragon, and one wrestled an ogre. When the knights returned to the castle they told their tales to the jester who was supposed to tell the king. But now the jester's all jumbled. From the clues below, help him sort out who did what.

Use the chart to keep track of your answers. Put an X in each box that can't be true and a circle in the boxes that match.

1. The princess wants to get engaged to her rescuer.
2. The ogre was waiting in a tall tower.
3. Sagamore and Parsifal are both happily married.
4. The knight whose name begins with the twelfth letter of the alphabet brought back the Grail.
5. Parsifal ended his quest in a cave.

	Dragon	Grail	Ogre	Princess
Bedivere				
Lancelot				
Parsifal				
Sagamore				

Answer on page 47.

Illustrated by Liisa Chauncy Guida

GLOBE PROBE

That intrepid explorer Cincinnati Holmes has seen so much of the wide world that he sometimes forgets where he is. On these pages are some of the unique ways in which Cincy has viewed his maps. See if you can guess in which country Dr. Holmes is located on each map, as shown by the X.

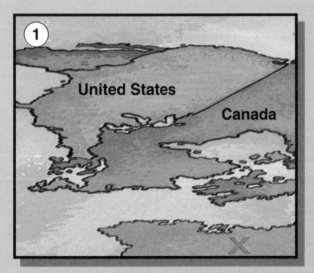

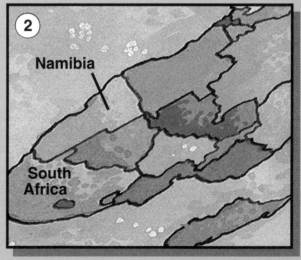

Illustrated by Jon Nez

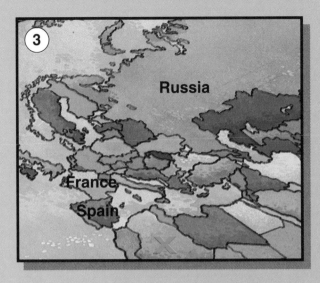

3 Russia
France
Spain

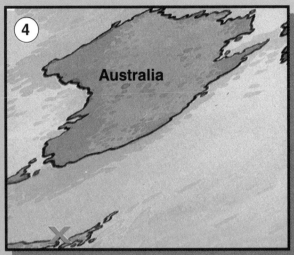

4 Australia

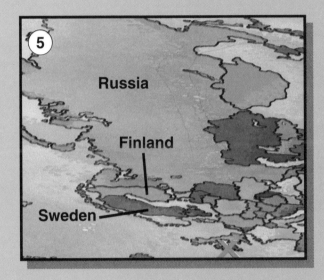

5 Russia
Finland
Sweden

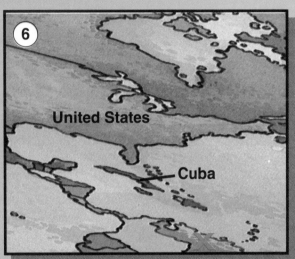

6 United States
Cuba

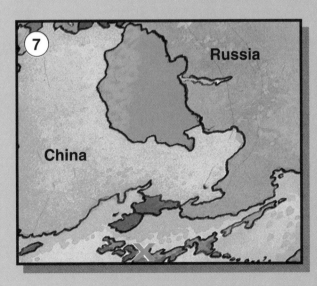

7 Russia
China

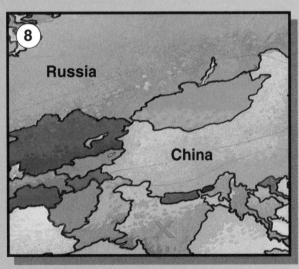

8 Russia
China

SCRAMBLED SENSE

Every word below can be unscrambled to make another word. The new words in each group all have something in common. Can you make sense of the groups?

1. Thorn
   Shout
   Stew
   Teas

2. Mar
   Gel
   Earth
   Inch

3. Tab
   Act
   Art
   Reed

4. Cheap
   Reap
   Melon
   Mile

5. Chin
   Dray
   Lime
   Race

Illustrated by Paul Richer

Answer on page 48

▮NSTANT PICTURE

To find out what's hidden on this page, fill in each section that contains two dots.

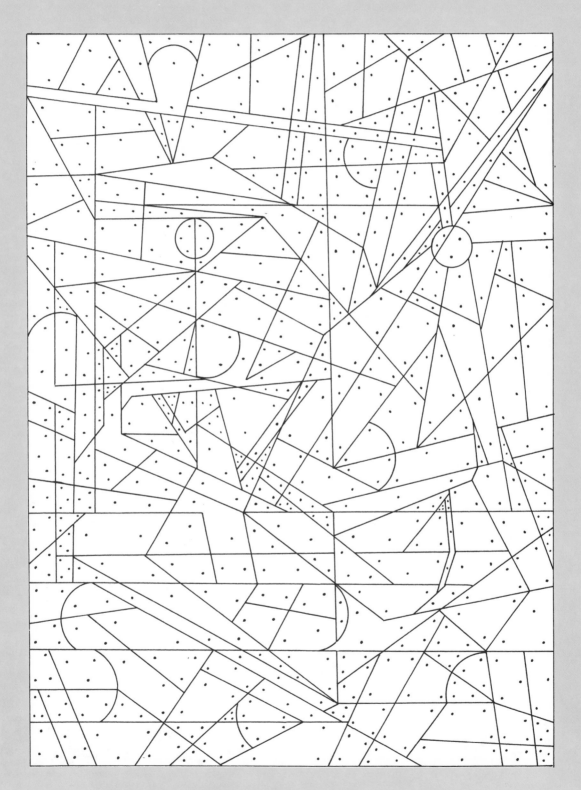

Illustrated by Rob Sepanak

SUNKEN SNAPSHOTS

While scuba diving in the South Seas, Sarah snapped some shots of her magnificent underwater adventure. But now she can't remember how the pictures go together. Can you figure out which order they go in so that Sarah can remember her trip? Hint: Sarah remembers that C is the first photo in the trail.

Illustrated by Judith Hunt

Answer on page 48.

WHAT AM I?

Can you guess the answer
before you reach the last clue?

I was first shown to Americans in 1886.

A. G. Eiffel, the same man who designed the Eiffel Tower, designed my interior structure.

My tablet reads July IV MDCCLXXVI.

I am just over 151 feet tall.

The area where you can find me was originally called Bedloe's Island.

I was a gift from France.

Emma Lazarus wrote a poem about me.

My real name is "Liberty Enlightening the World."

What am I?

Answer on page 48.

PARADE MEMORIES

Take a long look at this picture. Try to remember everything you see in it. Then turn the page and try to answer some questions without looking back at the picture.

Illustrated by Jon Davis

DON'T READ THIS UNTIL YOU HAVE LOOKED AT "Parade Memories—Part I" ON PAGE 15.

PARADE MEMORIES

Part II

Can you answer these questions about the parade scene you saw? Don't peek!

1. How many cameras can be seen at the parade?
2. What color uniform is the cymbal player wearing?
3. What was printed on the boy's tanktop?
4. Were any United States flags colored incorrectly?
5. How many balloons can you see at the parade?
6. Were there more men or women looking out the windows?
7. How many drummers were in this part of the band?
8. Were there any animals in the scene?

Answer on page 48.

BOX QUOTE

Can you discover what simple saying is hidden here? The letters from each column fit into the boxes directly above them to form words. Move the letters up to the right blanks, but be careful. The letters do not always go in the boxes in the same order as they appear. Each letter will be used only once, so cross it off as you put it in a box. The black boxes show the ends of words and get no letters. When all the letters are filled in correctly, you should be able to read a fun quote.

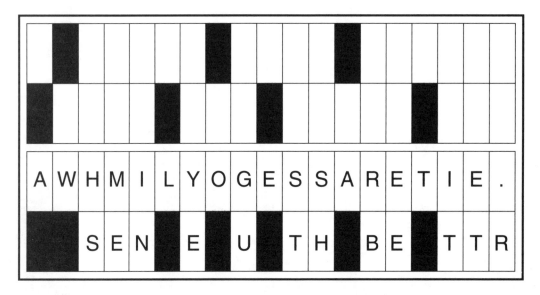

Answer on page 48.

DOT MAGIC

Connect the dots to see one of the wonders of the ancient world.

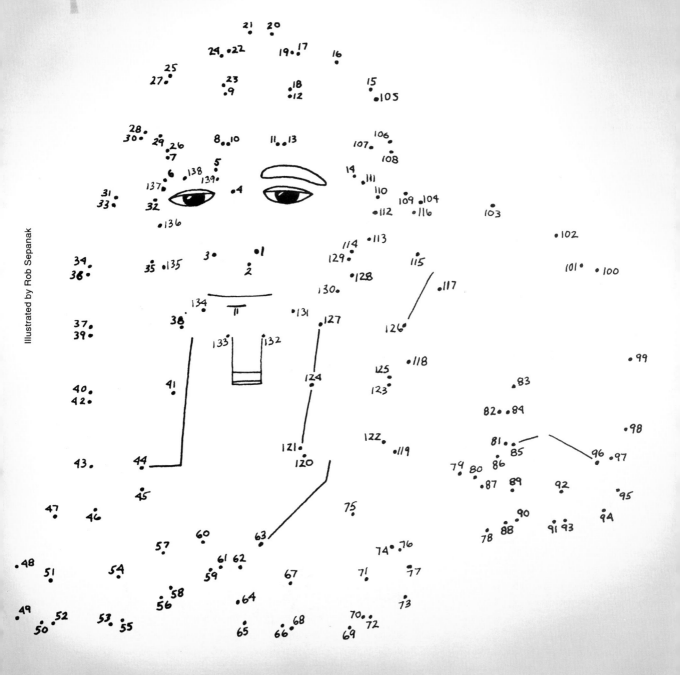

Illustrated by Rob Sepanak

HIDDEN PICTURES

There are at least 28 objects hidden in this picture. How many can you find?

Hot Dogs $1.50

HOGGING THE LIMELIGHT

How many differences can you spot between these two pictures?

WHICH IS MORE?

Can you tell which of these columns
will give you the largest answer?

I

Number of Snow White's dwarfs.

Minus the number of little pigs.

Multiplied by the number of Santa's reindeer (without Rudolph).

Divided by the number of singers in a quartet.

TOTAL:_____

II

Number of days it rained on Noah.

Minus a baker's dozen.

Divided by the number of bears in the Goldilocks story.

Plus the number of stars on the Israeli flag.

TOTAL: _____

III

Number of days in April.

Divided by the number of kittens who lost their mittens.

Minus the number of golden rings in the Christmas song.

Plus the number of natural wonders in the world.

TOTAL: _____

Illustrated by Gregg Valley

Answer on page 48.

THE WHEEL THING

This puzzle is really getting around. See if you can use the code
below to solve the riddles on the next page.

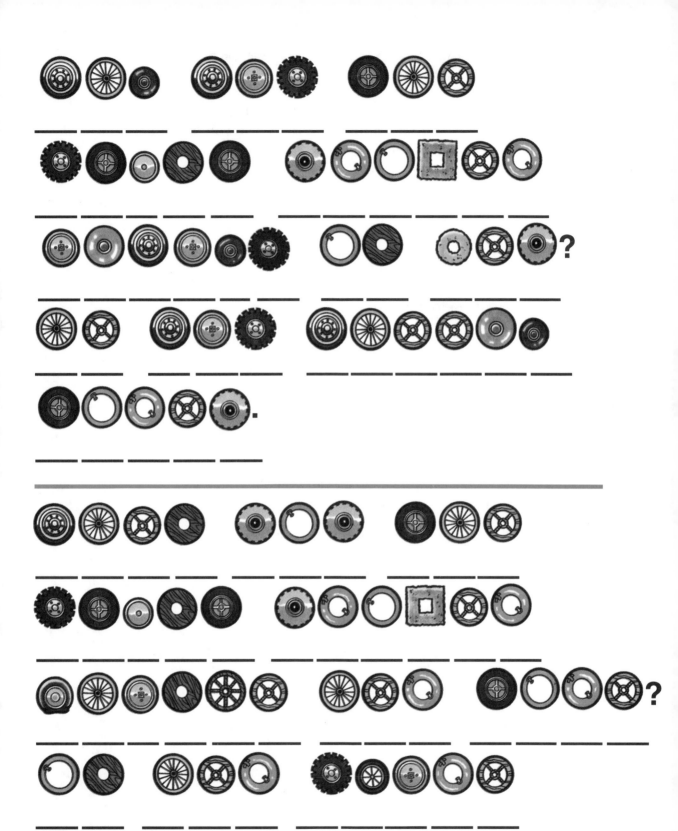

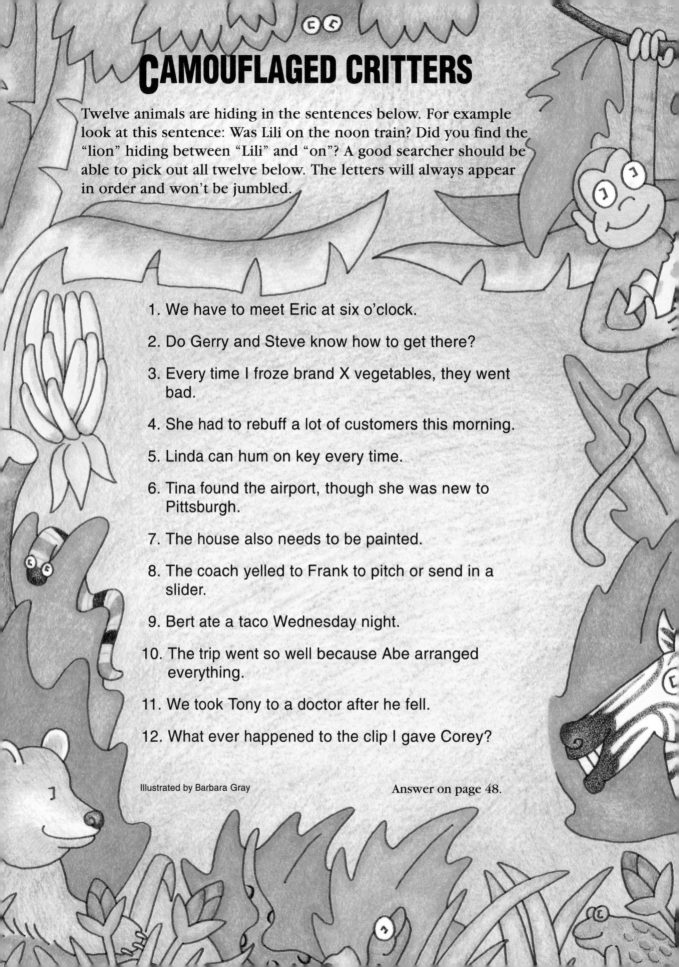

CAMOUFLAGED CRITTERS

Twelve animals are hiding in the sentences below. For example look at this sentence: Was Lili on the noon train? Did you find the "lion" hiding between "Lili" and "on"? A good searcher should be able to pick out all twelve below. The letters will always appear in order and won't be jumbled.

1. We have to meet Eric at six o'clock.

2. Do Gerry and Steve know how to get there?

3. Every time I froze brand X vegetables, they went bad.

4. She had to rebuff a lot of customers this morning.

5. Linda can hum on key every time.

6. Tina found the airport, though she was new to Pittsburgh.

7. The house also needs to be painted.

8. The coach yelled to Frank to pitch or send in a slider.

9. Bert ate a taco Wednesday night.

10. The trip went so well because Abe arranged everything.

11. We took Tony to a doctor after he fell.

12. What ever happened to the clip I gave Corey?

Illustrated by Barbara Gray

Answer on page 48.

WE URN IT

This ancient jug was recently uncovered in the Puzzlemania archaeological digs. It's so old that the design has been worn away. See if you can spruce it up by adding a new scene or design.

Illustrated by Kit Wray

FARM CHARM

Professor Hink Pink is back, spending his time searching for rhymes. He took a look at this farm with some charm. There is a tea tree and a goose with juice. How many other rhymes can you find?

Illustrated by Terry Rogers

Answer on page 48.

DINNER GUESS

These pictures are out of order. Can you number them to show
what happened first, second, and so on?

Illustrated by Jon Nez

Answer on page 49.

CHECK YOUR HAT

Check out all the different HAT words that make up this puzzle.

1. A short talk: ___ hat

2. Question word: ___ hat

3. Short door on a ship: hat ___ ___

4. Grainy roofs of old England: ___ hat ___ ___

5. Mad character from "Alice in Wonderland":
   Hat___ ___ ___

6. Where a magician hides his rabbit:
   ___ ___ ___ hat

7. Protective helmet for construction workers:
   ___ ___ ___ ___ hat

8. Type of cymbal: ___ ___ ___ ___ hat

9. French palace: ___ hât ___ ___ ___

10. A small hand axe: hat ___ ___ ___ ___

11. Smash or break: ___ hat ___ ___ ___

12. Score three goals in one game:
    hat ___ ___ ___ ___ ___

13. City in southeastern Tennessee that gave its name
    to a train:
    ___ hat ___ ___ ___ ___ ___ ___ ___

14. National seashore site off North Carolina:
    ___ ___ ___ ___ Hat ___ ___ ___ ___ ___

Answer on page 49.

Illustrated by Rich Johnson

JUST FOR LAUGHS

Some very funny words are hidden in the grid on the next page. See how many you can find by looking up, down, across, backward, and diagonally. Be careful because many letters appear in more than one word.

Absurd
Amuse
Bit
Cackle
Chuckle
Clown
Comedian
Comedy

Farce
Fun
Gag
Giggle
Glee
Grin
Guffaw
Ha-Ha

Happy
Jest
Joke
Jolly
Joy
Knock-knock
Laugh

Laughter
Mirth
Play
Prank
Pun
Quip
Riddle
Skit

Smile
Smirk
Stunt
Surprise
Tickle
Vaudeville

Illustrated by Terry Kovalcik

```
V A U D E V I L L E G M
M X M R W E C R A F I I
E S T U N T J K U U G R
L K I S S B N G A G T
K I C B Y E I O H K L H
C T K A C J T C T R E C
U Y L L O J O K E I E A
H P E Y M M S K R M L C
C P Z G E N M N Q S D K
L A U D D I I O Z U D L
O H I N Y R L C D T I E
W A F F U G E K N A R P
N H T L S U R P R I S E
```

Answer on page 49.

TRAFFIC JAM

There's no reason to rush through this puzzle. How many matching cars can you find? How many trucks?

LANGUAGE ARTS

In this frame is a masterpiece. All you need to do is write down as many words as you can from the letters in MASTERPIECE and it will be complete. Words should be three letters or longer, and they should not end in plural "s." We mastered this piece with over 100 words. How many can you find?

_____

_____

_____

_____

_____

_____

_____

_____

_____

_____

_____

Illustrated by Teresa Howell

PICTURE MIXER

Copy these mixed-up squares in the spaces on the next page to put this picture back together. The letters and numbers tell you where each square belongs. The first one, A-3, has been done for you.

A-3 A-4 A-2 A-1

B-2 B-4 B-1 B-3

C-2 C-4 C-3 C-1

D-4 D-3 D-1 D-2

Answer on page 49.

	1	2	3	4
A				
B				
C				
D				

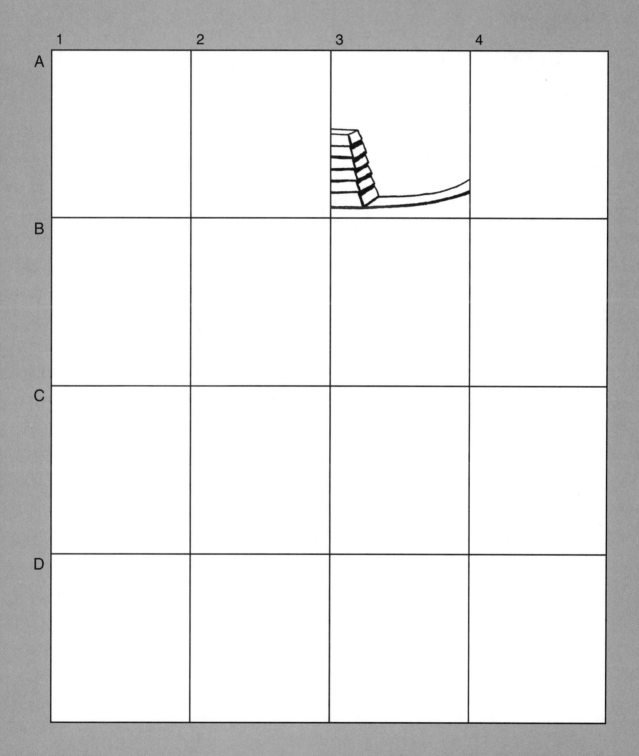

Illustrated by Rob Sepanak

KNIT KNOTS

These knitting nannies are working overtime.
Can you tell which knitter is using which ball of yarn?

Illustrated by Jerry Zimmerman

STOP, LOOK, AND LIST

Under each category, list one thing that begins with each letter. For example, one part of a car that begins with "C" is the clutch. See if you can name another.

PARTS OF A CAR

C _____

B _____

A _____

E _____

S _____

STORYBOOK FEMALES

C _____

B _____

A _____

E _____

S _____

SOUTH AMERICAN COUNTRIES

C _____

B _____

A _____

E _____

S _____

Illustrated by Lisa Dayer

Answer on page 50.

INSIDE JOB

Each object on the left-hand page belongs inside one of the objects on the right-hand page. Use your wits to get inside the problem and make the matches.

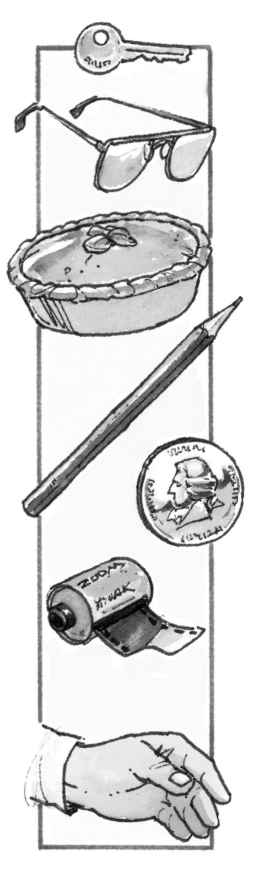

Illustrated by Jon Davis

Answer on page 50.

BRICK-A-BRAC

There is quite a load of bricks in this wall,
but how many of them have exactly four sides?

Illustrated by Kit Wray
Answer on page 50.

ODD ONE OUT

One word in each category isn't quite right. Can you tell which one it is and why it doesn't belong?

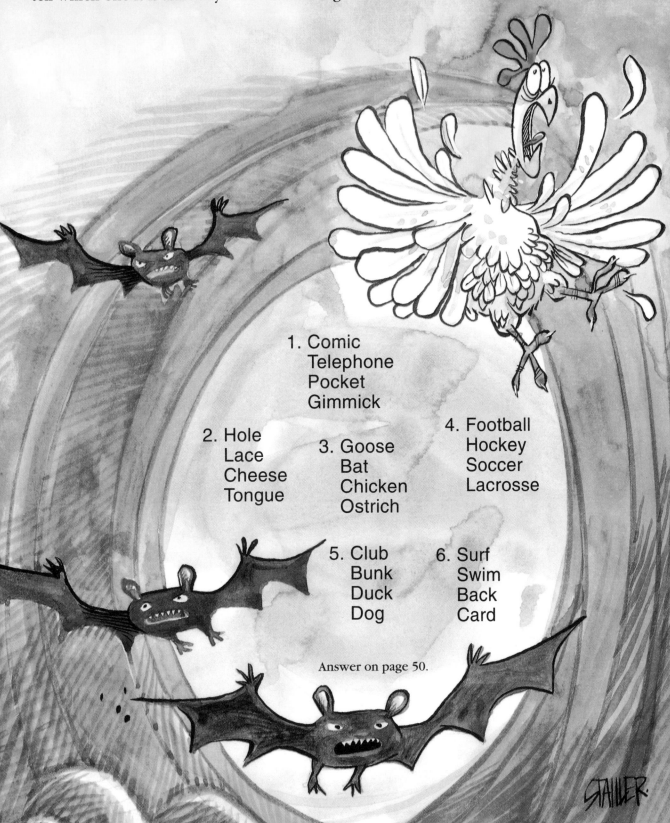

1. Comic
   Telephone
   Pocket
   Gimmick

2. Hole
   Lace
   Cheese
   Tongue

3. Goose
   Bat
   Chicken
   Ostrich

4. Football
   Hockey
   Soccer
   Lacrosse

5. Club
   Bunk
   Duck
   Dog

6. Surf
   Swim
   Back
   Card

Answer on page 50.

VOWELS NOW

A lot of the names of the items in this picture begin with a vowel (a, e, i, o, or u). If you can find at least 26, give yourself an A+.

LET'S GO TO A . . .

Now that you've almost finished all the great puzzles in this book, you may be looking for something else to do. Below is a list of fun places to visit. Set up your travels by putting the words in the right spaces on the map. No letters have been filled in yet, but use the size of the words as clues to where they might go. It may help to cross each word off the list once you put it in the puzzle.

3 LETTERS
Gym

4 LETTERS
Camp
City
Club
Game
Mall
Park
Play
Pool
Race
Show

5 LETTERS
Beach
Dance
Movie
Opera
Party
Roast
Track

6 LETTERS
Ballet
Circus
Market
Museum
Parade
Picnic

7 LETTERS
Concert
Cookout
Gallery
Stadium

8 LETTERS
Ballgame
Carnival
Monument

10 LETTERS
Restaurant

11 LETTERS
Sports Event

Answer on page 50.

ROW, ROW, ROW

Each cake below has something in common with the two others in the same row. For example, in the top row across there is writing on each cake. Look at the other rows across, down, and diagonally. Can you tell what each row of cakes has in common?

Illustrated by Anni Matsick

Answer on page 50.

ANSWERS

COVER

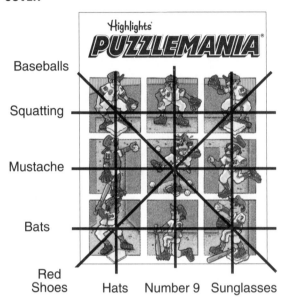

Baseballs
Squatting
Mustache
Bats
Red Shoes — Hats — Number 9 — Sunglasses

FOUR-LETTER WORDS (pages 4-5)

ROUTE TO THE RING (page 6)

QUEST WHO? (page 7)

If the princess wants to get engaged to her rescuer (clue 1), the rescuer could not have been Sagamore or Parsifal, who are both married (clue 3). The twelfth letter of the alphabet is L, therefore Lancelot brought home the Grail (clue 4), and did not rescue the princess, which leaves only Bedivere. This leaves only Sagamore and Parsifal. If Parsifal ended his quest in a cave (clue 5), he could not have captured the ogre in the tower (clue 2). And so Sagamore must have wrestled the ogre, while Parsifal captured the dragon.

GLOBE PROBE (pages 8-9)

1. Greenland
2. Madagascar
3. Algeria
4. New Zealand
5. Ireland
6. Venezuela
7. Japan
8. India

SCRAMBLED SENSE (page 10)

1. north, south, west, and east - directions
2. arm, leg, heart, chin - parts of the body
3. bat, cat, rat, deer - animals or mammals
4. peach, pear, lemon, lime - fruit
5. inch, yard, mile, acre - units of measurement

INSTANT PICTURE (page 11)

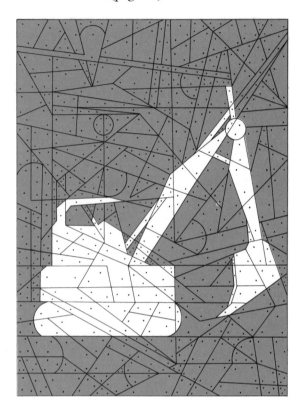

SUNKEN SNAPSHOTS (pages 12-13)

A. 4	E. 8	I. 3
B. 7	F. 6	J. 12
C. 1	G. 9	K. 2
D. 11	H. 10	L. 5

WHAT AM I? (page 14)
The Statue of Liberty

PARADE MEMORIES (page 16)

1. One
2. Blue
3. Go!
4. Yes, one in window
5. Nine
6. Men
7. One
8. No

BOX QUOTE (page 16)
A smile gets better when you share it.

DOT MAGIC (page 17)

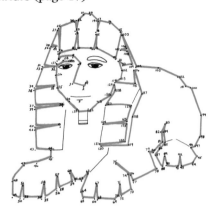

WHICH IS MORE? (page 21)

Column I:	Column II:	Column III:
7-3=4	40-13=27	30÷3=10
4x8=32	27÷3=9	10-5=5
32÷4=**8**	9+1=**10**	5+7=**12**

Column III has the largest answer.

THE WHEEL THING (pages 22-23)
Why was the stunt driver always in bed?
He was wheely tired.

When did the stunt driver change her tire?
In her spare time.

CAMOUFLAGED CRITTERS (page 24)

1. cat (between Eric and at)
2. dog (between Do and Gerry
3. zebra (between froze and brand)
4. buffalo (between rebuff, a, and lot)
5. monkey (between hum, on , and key)
6. newt (between new and to)
7. seal (between house and also)
8. horse (between pitch, or, and send)
9. cow (between taco and Wednesday)
10. bear (between Abe and arranged)
11. toad (between to, a, and doctor)
12. pig (between clip, I, and gave)

FARM CHARM (pages 26-27)

Crane Vane	Ants Pants
House Mouse	Blue Shoe
Cat Bat	Ten Hens
Eggs Legs	Barn Yarn
Porch Torch	Goose Juice
Bale Scale or Weigh Hay	Lance Pants
Goat Coat	Mad Pad
Tea Tree	Door Four
Potatoes Tomatoes	Note Coat
Chair Pair	Eye Tie
Cents Fence	

DINNER GUESS (page 28)

4   3
6   2
1   5

CHECK YOUR HAT (page 29)

1. chat
2. what
3. hatch
4. thatch
5. Hatter
6. top hat
7. hardhat
8. highhat
9. château
10. hatchet
11. shatter
12. hat trick
13. Chattanooga
14. Cape Hatteras

JUST FOR LAUGHS (pages 30-31)

TRAFFIC JAM (page 32)

LANGUAGE ARTS (page 33)

We found 168 words. You may have found others.

ace	crime	pare	recite	steam
aid	ear	part	remit	steamer
aim	ease	past	repeat	steep
ampere	east	paste	rest	steer
ape	easter	pat	rice	step
arc	eat	pea	rim	stir
are	epee	peace	ripe	strap
arid	era	pear	rise	stream
arm	esteem	peer	rite	strip
art	ice	perm	same	stripe
asp	imp	pert	sat	tame
aster	irate	pest	scare	tap
ate	ire	pica	scram	tape
cam	item	pie	scrap	tar
came	mace	piece	scrape	tarp
camp	map	pier	scream	tea
cap	mar	pierce	sea	team
cape	mare	pirate	seam	tear
caper	mart	pit	sear	tease
car	maser	pita	seat	tee
care	mast	price	see	temper
carp	master	priest	seer	term
carpet	mat	prim	sir	tie
case	mate	prime	sire	tier
cast	meat	prism	sit	time
caste	mere	raise	site	timer
cat	merit	ram	space	trace
cater	mice	ramp	spare	traipse
cease	miser	rap	spear	trap
cramp	mist	rat	spice	tree
crate	mister	rate	stamp	trim
cream	miter	ream	stair	trip
crease	pace	reap	star	
create	par	recipe	stare	

PICTURE MIXER (pages 34-35)

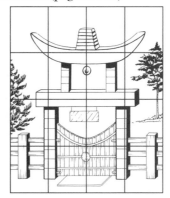

KNIT KNOTS (page 36)
A-4   B-1   C-2   D-3

STOP, LOOK, AND LIST (page 37)
These are the answers we found. You may have found others.

Parts of a Car
Carburetor
Brakes
Axle
Engine
Steering Wheel

Storybook Females
Charlotte (*Charlotte's Web*)
Beth (*Little Women*)
Alice (*Alice in Wonderland*)
Em (*Wizard of Oz*)
Snow White (*Snow White*)

South American Countries
Colombia
Brazil
Argentina
Ecuador
Suriname

INSIDE JOB (pages 38-39)
key - lock
straw - bottle of soda
eyeglasses - case
picture - frame
letter - mailbox
tape - dispenser
cufflinks - sleeve
bird - cage
pie - oven
pencil - sharpener
train - tunnel
coin - telephone
film - camera
hand - glove

BRICK-A-BRAC (page 40)

ODD ONE OUT (page 41)
1. gimmick — others are books
2. cheese — others are parts of shoes
3. Bat is the only mammal — others are birds
4. football — scores are called goals in others
5. duck — all the others are houses
6. swim — others are prefixes for board

LET'S GO TO A... (pages 44-45)

ROW, ROW, ROW (page 46)

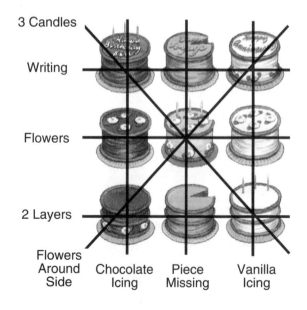